99 Interruptions

C000092428

Charles Boyle was
published poetry,
founded the small

From reviews of *The Other Jack: A book about books, mostly*

'The book presents as a wash of short, wide-ranging passages on books, writing, publishing and reading, lightly written and deeply thoughtful, with a wonderful index of literary concerns. At the beginning of the book, Robyn has somehow identified Charles as the author, under his pseudonym Jack Robinson, of some of her favourite books, and Charles's relationship to this Jack, and his long history as a writer and as the germ and motor of CB editions is seamlessly conjoined both with his history as a reader and lover of books and with what we could call, for want of a better term, his social conscience.' – Thomas Koed, *Volume*

'Whatever a novel is, I feel this is what I want a novel now to be.' – Jane Feaver

by the same author

CHARLES BOYLE
The Disguise: Poems 1977–2001
The Other Jack: A book about books, mostly

Writing as JENNIE WALKER
24 for 3

Writing as JACK ROBINSON
Days and Nights in W12
Robinson
An Overcoat: Scenes from the Afterlife of H.B.
Good Morning, Mr Crusoe
Blush (with Natalia Zagórska-Thomas)

99 Interruptions

Charles Boyle

CB editions

First published in Great Britain in 2022
by CB editions
146 Percy Road London W12 9QL
www.cbeditions.com

© Charles Boyle, 2022

Cover: Francisco José de Goya y Lucientes, *Valentias? Quenta
los annos!* ('Showing off? Remember your age!'), *c.*1816–20.
Copyright: bpk / Kupferstichkabinett, SMB / Jörg P. Anders

The right of Charles Boyle to be identified as author
of this work has been identified in accordance with
Section 77 of the Copyright, Designs and Patents Act 1988

Printed in England by Imprint Digital, Exeter

ISBN 978-1-909585-50-8

1   *Pray my Dear, have you not forgot to wind up the clock?*

2   Odysseus gets up in the morning and checks the weather (cloudy, occasional showers) and thinks: So what storm/shipwreck/weird-tasting fruit/man-eating giant is in store for me today? He's tired, his bones are aching, he has spent ten years fighting a war and he just wants to go home.

3   Few people trust straight lines. Work hard and you'll get your just reward? A likely story. Stonemasons add gargoyles. Politicians add bad jokes. Bridget Riley adds swerves and dissonance. Writers whose protagonists are seeking true love, or to solve a crime or kill a dragon or rescue a princess, add in pratfalls, red herrings and interruptions along the way. Without a kink in the line there's no story to tell. The kinks *are* the story.

4   Lovers entangled in bed hear the front door opening . . . If the lovers are seventeen, this will be parents coming home early (Dad ordered the shellfish; Mum found the play so boring they left at the interval); if they are in their forties, it will be the children sent home from school for wearing the wrong shoes. If this is a novel, it will be a husband or a wife, or at least an interested partner. Then a phone rings – but they can ignore this, it's only a marketing survey – and then, as footsteps approach along the corridor or up the stairs, the sublime becomes ridiculous: trousers, skirts, zips, buttons, a lover hidden inside a wardrobe or under the bed or perched on the windowsill, knowing that when they jump they will break at least an ankle.

5   Sometimes the interrupter is an Amazon delivery guy and sometimes it's Azrael, the angel of death. In Jean-Philippe Toussaint's *The Truth about Marie*, Marie stands naked in her bedroom at 3 o'clock in the morning as five paramedics attempt in vain to resuscitate her lover. In Javier Marías' *Tomorrow in the Battle Think on Me* a woman dies before she and her lover have even finished undressing each other. In both novels these are the opening scenes: getting the interruption in early.

6   Death is not funny. Death is not a *line break*.
But there are people whose immediate response to a
traumatic experience is to giggle, and I can understand
that.

7   Bugs Bunny is running for dear life, running so fast
he doesn't notice he's run over the edge of a cliff – and
for as long as his forward momentum lasts his legs are
still pumping, frantic, until he looks down: oh.

Meanwhile, inland, at junctions and on bridges and
slip roads Extinction Rebellion stages interruptions in
the steady flow of traffic towards the cliff edge. While
the police work out how to un-glue the protesters from
the road the drivers in the backed-up cars and vans are
checking their watches, phoning in to say they'll be
late, picking their noses, *scratching*, listening to music,
remembering last night or a Saturday afternoon in the
1970s, composing villanelles or letters to the editor,
worrying about their swollen testicles or the lumps on
their breasts or the flashing red light on the dashboard,
watching porn and knitting bonnets and eating cheese-
and-pickle sandwiches and checking the cricket scores
and silently weeping and planning the perfect murder
and counting sheep.

8   Interruptions are quick-fire switches of register and
like banana skins are essentially (to the audience) comic.

Interruptions mock habit and routine and complacency. Interruptions are gentle or not-so-gentle reminders that we have no God-given right to be here at all. Interruptions are the jokers in the pack. The children playing with a ball on the terrace of the fancy restaurant are interruptions-waiting-to-happen, and men in business suits give their mothers hard looks: *Why can't they keep their nuisances in line?*

9   Just as it starts to rain my father comes into the café. He is wearing a tie – except for when he was in the bath or on the beach at Filey, I cannot remember seeing him without one. He sits down at my table and asks what kind of car I'm driving these days and when I tell him I don't have a car he looks disappointed. My father liked his cars; his last was an olive-green Riley. He's been dead for 65 years. He's a rain god now.

10   Slapstick: the deadpan heroes of silent comedy films* cannot walk down a street without being whacked by a plank, or enter a room without getting a pie in their face. This is recognition comedy: there but for the grace

---

* Films used to demand that I watch them in one sitting, usually in a building called the Odeon. And stand for the national anthem while the credits rolled. And not on Sundays. There was a lot of *not*. It's only recently that their delivery system has caught up with that of books, allowing me to pause, rewind and fast-forward in bed.

of God go I. But as one interruption follows another, what's funny becomes not the interruptions themselves but their evasion: the pie in the face of the other guy, the guy behind the guy who's just ducked; Buster Keaton walking away scot-free from a house wall that's fallen on him because he happens to be standing in the space of an open window. In the scene in *Modern Times* in which Charlie Chaplin as a waiter carries a tray of food and drink held high overhead in one hand through a crowded and lively dance floor, what's funny is that he *gets there*, to the diner's table, achieving what he's set out to do without (bar a chicken impaled on a candelabra) major interruption. Odysseus has arrived in Ithaca.

11 A rabbit is interrupted by a duck, and vice versa. Rage is interrupted by laughter, and vice versa. Joy is interrupted by grief, hunger by disgust, words by silence. Ecclesiastes was up for this, the full range of contradictory human behaviour, but his own formulation – a time to mourn and a time to dance, a time to embrace and a time to refrain from embracing – sounds like a school timetable: sewing on Tuesday mornings, rending on Wednesday afternoons. There *is* a time for most everything but what Ecclesiastes misses is that we are not good at getting our timing right. I weep when I should be angry, I walk away when I should be approaching. So many of the tributes to the comedians of yesteryear mention their subjects' matchless 'sense of timing'. We measure out our lives in obituaries of people who have made us laugh.

12   Bad timing while crossing the road and you can end up in hospital in a coma. More bad timing, wrong accent, a face that fits, and you can be put away for a crime you didn't commit . . . That man who hadn't got the right paperwork and was stuck in Charles de Gaulle airport for 18 years. That soldier who didn't get the message that Japan had surrendered at the end of World War Two and who hid out in the jungle in the Philippines for 29 years. What the precise numbers indicate is the banality of interruptions. I assume, of course, that at some never-precisely-dated point the interrupted life becomes simply the life as lived, and that the arrival of correct paperwork for man-in-airport, or news of end of hostilities for man-in-jungle, would have come as a secondary interruption, to be resisted.

13   My father gets out a pack of cigarettes and looks around for an ashtray. I tell him we can't smoke in here; we can smoke at the tables outside but it's raining, so we're just going to have to wait. He looks at me as if I am a complete stranger. After this long we *are* strangers – in truth we always were: we didn't share enough time to get to know each other – and I warn him that in these pages there's going to be stuff about books, because I'm a bookaholic, and though they're less likely to kill me than cigarettes and alcohol my addiction is still a troubling thing: joy, dependence, sometimes rage.* My father nods, slowly. He was never much of a reader. He may be regretting that he came into the café. I ask him if he's met any deceased writers and how they are getting on, whether they too have regrets, whether they think they wasted their lives, and he replies that it's not his field and besides, that's not how the afterlife works. To assume he knows more than me, or has access to more information, is as daft as assuming that just because I've lived longer and later I know more than him.

14 What keeps me honest? Toast. Mountains, maybe. Rivers, lakes, moors. (But why is it so *quiet*?) Being told that I'm wrong. Good people. Good writing, good art. And hiccups. Toothache. Farts. Interruptions. The dog turd I step into on the pavement outside my front door, the 'technical fault' further up the line, the website that

---

* A scene in a novel I read decades ago: a man sweeping all the books on his shelves to the floor. It was biblical. It was like that scene in films in which a deeply frustrated character hurls whatever is in their hand – a glass, a plate, a smartphone, a book, a child's toy – against a wall and it shatters a mirror and then why not, go for it, and everything else follows, whatever's in arm's reach, sheer destruction, whatever it takes to break through to the other side, as if there *is* another side, and the character is left trembling and exhausted. Cut.

crashes when I try to buy a ticket, the thunderstorm
that puts paid to England's push for victory, the editors
who tell me my poems are 'not for us' – everything that
conspires to *get in the way* of plain sailing from A to B.*

15   My father smells of, I think, a 1950s aftershave. One
weekday afternoon in the 1950s the television arrived,
and the first programme I watched was *Andy Pandy*.
Flower Pot Men was better: Bill and Ben live in flower
pots, as Nagg and Nell live in dustbins in Beckett's
Endgame, and speak in a nonsense version of English
called Oddle Poddle that makes complete sense. As I
concentrate on the smell of my father's aftershave it fades
to nothing, like the dot on a cathode-ray TV screen faded
to nothing when you switched it off. It was saying: Please
don't go yet, keep me company, watch me disappear first.
So I did.

16   An ordinary young woman is going about her
day – hanging out the washing is how I sometimes see
her – when suddenly an angel appears and tells her she
will soon become pregnant with the Son of God. How
does she know he's an angel, and not just another guy
from the rugby club? Because he's got strap-on wings? It

---

* Setting out from A, why am I so sure that B is where I want to get
to anyway?

could happen to anyone. Interruptions are nothing if not democratic.

17   The advertising that comprises so much of urban scenery is less an interruption of my view than the view itself. It's wallpaper. I am not going to buy that car or that deodorant, obviously. They know this. They know that I know they know this. They just want to remind me that the people in charge here are the people who are selling things.

When I do experience ads as interruptive I'm invited to pay money to block them. Money jumps queues, cuts through red tape, buys visas, buys insurance against theft and loss and blocked drains.* No wonder the rich are so stupid.

18   Their teeth are very white. Their skin is smooth. Their smiles are undiluted. The models in the clothing catalogues and in the ads for package holidays and business software and life insurance and retirement homes are Stepford Wives, both the men and the women. Also the Photoshopped people in the projections of what's coming next on the hoardings of redevelopment sites: shopping and coffee, shopping and coffee, until

---

* But not 'acts of God'. Old Him with His thunderbolts is still around, signed up by the insurance companies as a get-out clause and pocketing a commission on every rejected claim.

orange juice and yoga in the retirement homes, and no need for irony because selling a pup – this user-friendly, seamless, interruption-less fantasy – works fine without. We *like* buying puppies.

19   I stroke my life, feed it, smooth down the rough bits and take it for walks. I *story* it. Sometimes it bites back.

20   In order to be interrupted I have to be going somewhere, even if only downstairs. Or to at least have a *train of thought* – and I do, I think I'm onto something here – don't interrupt me – but there, I've already interrupted myself and I've lost the thread. Self-interrupting is often an expression of my instinct for self-preservation: *Slow down, you're going too fast, you'll only fall over and get hurt.* I have an equal and opposite instinct for self-destruction. First one and then the other, constantly interrupting each other. Boom and bust, boom and bust.

21   Each time I place my bookmark (envelope, till receipt) in a book* I am marking the page where my reading has been interrupted – by the train or bus

---

* Or turn down the corner of a page. Turned-down corners in second-hand books are humdrum mysteries: what exactly called the reader away? Did they ever come back?

arriving at my stop, by food being served up, by a phone call from my brother, by tiredness, by the Amazon delivery guy again (the package is for next door, but they're out), by sex, by the dog being sick on the hearthrug or the cat scratching at the window to be let in, very often by another book that calls to me more urgently than the one in my hands . . . Very few books are read 'in a single sitting', as excited reviewers sometimes claim: not even a toilet break? A book being read is a continuous narrative interrupted by quotidian demands; or it is my stop-start progress through the day interrupted by sections of continuous narrative.

22   Sometimes I'm so engrossed in a book that I ride past my bus or tube stop and find myself somewhere I hadn't planned on being. This is another kind of interruption. Stepping out, I feel I've absconded, that I'm playing truant. Wide open.

23   A book, then – even one as short as this – is an interruption which is often itself interrupted. While I'm reading it, my life is on hold; while I'm getting on with my life, the book is on hold. Iseult (in Elizabeth Bowen's *Eva Trout*) puts it strongly: 'Life is an anti-novel.' She sounds disappointed; she is renewing contact with another character she hasn't seen for years and is reflecting on the fact that nothing between them appears to have changed; as a reader of novels, change and 'development' are what she has learned to expect, what keep her turning the pages. But frankly life doesn't give a fig about novels, it's the other way round: novels, engineered by a meaning-seeking, pattern-making species, are a revenge upon life.

24 Like life, to which they claim fidelity, novels generally proceed from one interruption to another (storms, sudden deaths, the stranger in the night); unlike life, novels get their ducks *in a row*: the interruptions are pre-packaged and tucked in. Novels shape the one-damn-thing-after-another that is life into a work of art which is then offered back to the world as a performative interruption.*

25 Interruptions – feral, unpredictable – knock me off course. There are times when I guard against this: I set off early to get to the airport, I don't want to be still in the queue at security when the last call for my flight is announced, I'd prefer to be one of the smug folk

---

* Novelists are often more troubled by this than readers; many break the fourth wall (not a modern thing: see Stendhal, Sterne, Thackeray) by addressing the reader directly, effectively saying: This is only a story. To which the reader replies: I know that but tell me what happens next.

lounging at the departure gate and staring at the shoes of strangers. *Those are nice socks.* There are also times when being knocked off course is exactly what I want.*

Stevie Smith on the Person from Porlock: 'I am hungry to be interrupted / For ever and ever amen / O Person from Porlock come quickly / And bring my thoughts to an end.' Bear in mind that the Person from Porlock is likely to be smelly and tedious; and he (it was a him for Coleridge: 'detained by him above an hour') always arrives at an inconvenient time; but could just possibly be The One, which is why you open the door.

26   The child trips, falls, grazes a knee or an elbow. Mute shock, before the yell and the tears. There, *that* place: between what happens and the registering of what has happened and then the response. If it didn't pop like a bubble it would have to go on expanding, endlessly.

27   Children – the ones who know that if they trip and fall they will be picked up and comforted: not

---

* I *expect* to be interrupted. I expect the world to end (but not in my lifetime) and I expect to die (ditto). I may even believe that I deserve this. We (always a questionable pronoun) are good at self-loathing, and even better at taking this out on others – just as we are good at systematically destroying our own chances of survival on this planet, and at wasting our opportunities to make our societies more just and decent.

all – are good at happiness but for grown-ups whose instinct for happiness has been thwarted or tamped down it's scary. Do I deserve it? Who makes that judgement? If 'deserving' is irrelevant, is it just luck? Cue, for the unlucky, self-sabotage: addictions, self-harm, relationships with others who do damage, but it can also be done by simply glancing away or looking down, playing safe.

28 'America, fuckers! Russia, cunts!' the man at the back of the bus is shouting today. He is in pain. As he passes me on his way to get off the bus he quietly apologises for shouting. His first language is Croatian, his second is Serbian, but he can swear well enough in English. 'These fragments I have shored against my ruins.' 'Kubla Khan', the poem whose writing was interrupted by the Person from Porlock, was published in 1816 as 'A Fragment'. In the same year, for a knock-down price the British government purchased Lord Elgin's collection of damaged marble sculptures hacked off from the Parthenon in Athens and shipped to England. Fragments were becoming a cultural thing: not just work from the past surviving in incomplete form but also the deliberate construction of work that refuses connection and endings, that elevates interruption into an aesthetic principle.

29   Once it has interrupted, an interruption becomes part of the back-story; its push-back energy is absorbed into the forward momentum. From a long perspective, such as that from which I view the distant past, local interruptions are absorbed into larger patterns of progress or decline – X number of people per year fall down old wells or are killed in road accidents or civil wars but the human race staggers on – but right now any such long perspective feels like an improbable luxury.

30   Don't expect much about progress narratives in a book with the word 'interruptions' in its title. Except to say: the derailment of progress narratives leaves people confused as to whether they are going forwards or backwards. Are periods of social justice (relatively speaking) staging posts en route to a better world, or brief bucolic interludes in the long slide towards barbarism? Any Plan B needs to find a less binary way of addressing this.

31   Fall off your horse and most people standing around will tell you to get straight back in the saddle. Pick yourself up and carry on. Stay true to your goals (sometimes called dreams) and persevere. Giving up is perceived as weakness, even though there are times when it may be a perfectly reasonable or even liberating option. (Other goals/dreams are available.) A third option is to carry on but without really expecting to get anywhere. From an obituary tribute to a man who taught me Eng Lit at university: 'He loved doing things he could not quite do, such as writing fiction or playing the accordion.'

32   No, I sometimes needed to explain to my children as we sat on the sofa watching a wildlife documentary, those animals are not fighting, they are *mating*. Today I'm thinking that that's more apt for how novels relate to life than the outright antagonism perceived by Iseult. Every novel is a choreography of interruptions: not just internally, in its switches and switch-backs between narrative and reflection, dialogue and description, this character and that one, but in the to-and-fro of its relationship with life. Novels take from life but they also give: 'After reading Gogol one's eyes may become gogolized and one is apt to see bits of his world in the most unexpected places' (Nabokov). The relationship is beguiling because novels are made of the same material I use to inform and warn and plead and mislead and muddle through the day when I am not burying my head in a book; and because of my enduring ability to hold two (or more) contradictory beliefs in my mind at the same time. The grief I feel when a character I've grown to like is killed off is not less real for my knowing the character was fictitious.

33   As a bookish and quite solitary boy, I think I believed for some time that love was something that happened to characters in films and books, not to the likes of me (or to anyone else in the dormitory suburb of Leeds where I grew up). I could more easily imagine myself in a war than in love. Actors and other famous people fell in love, of course, and magazines in waiting rooms told their stories, but maybe the actors were simply acting out in life the roles they played on screen, and the other famous people aspired to be actors? Love as a kind of supreme fiction? It turns out I was wrong,* but I'm still a sucker for the kind of love stories that seem improbable: teenage sweethearts who marry others and then find each other together again after a

---

* If by 'love' I mean what was generally portrayed as such in books and films, then believing it wasn't a thing that happened to the likes of me was not entirely stupid. Love, the books had it, is transformative; only through love can people truly become themselves; love is the one Big Thing. Capitalism leant into this – individualism at the expense of community – and the marketing department went into overdrive, placing a burden of unrealistic expectation on both men and women. Vivian Gornick's *The End of the Novel of Love* has a chapter in which she demonstrates that the confused longing of male characters in stories by Raymond Carver, Richard Ford and Andre Dubus is for an idealised model of men–women relations that never really existed, and that rather than being a sympathetic trait – as the writers intended it to be – the men's confusion has damaged both themselves and their women. Admittedly, replacing perfect love with porn and novels featuring repetitive bad sex doesn't help anyone.

gap of decades, for example. Something quite ordinary here is magnified and made heroic by the length of the interruption. 'You couldn't make it up.'

34   A cheval glass, a feather toque with veil . . . I used to read novels not least for the props: the clothes, the furniture, the food, the cigarettes, the cars. It was like looking into a drawer in my mother's bedroom. I didn't know what most of these things were but they held the code for becoming a grown-up. Now I'm over three-score-and-ten I read new novels as code for being young, and it's indecipherable.

35   'La pluie, dans la cour où je la regarde tomber, descend à des allures très diverses . . .' That's Francis Ponge. There is rain and there is more rain and it's really just a bit of *weather*, water pouring through holes in the sky ('They're ever so small. That's why the rain is thin': Spike Milligan) but every poet has a poem about rain, they find it seriously sexy. It patters, putters, teems and streams and lashes, it flows and ebbs, it comes and goes and after a shower there's a quiet post-coital exhalation, glossy green leaves against a washed grey sky. In the rain poem by Borges (trans. Alastair Reid) the evening rain 'which spreads its blind across the pane' brings him the voice of his father: 'Who comes back now, who has never been dead.'

36   The occupants of the room, fourteen of them, are all male. I'm in that room, back in school; women are absent, women were distraction. Or interruption? (*Where are the women? At home? At school, in another room, being taught needlework?*) Heads down, these boys are as preoccupied in their studying as I am, studying them. Their concentration is as intense as that of the readers in the sublime book of photographs by André Kertész titled *On Reading*: photos of readers in parks and libraries, on beds and balconies and pavements and rooftops, oblivious to the churn of the world around them. What are they looking at, these boys, through their microscopes? The room is a laboratory and they are observing how some cells just get on with their jobs and some go rogue and who can tell why. They are *reading*.

37   My father is looking tired, as if it's past his bedtime. He is fiddling in his pockets – maybe he needs to take a pill. Interruptions are a part of the deal, I say, and exposure to them is a way of building up a healthy immune system. It didn't work for *me*, replies my father, who died of cancer, and then I notice that about a dozen people carrying umbrellas in many colours are looking at us through the café window. No, it is my father they are looking at. They are taking photos. They are tourists who have signed up for a local-history walk and the man with the clipboard who is their guide waves to my father and smiles. My father waves back. He's perking up.

38   After my father died, my mother was advised that
two practical ways of coping with grief are listening
to music and gardening, and she chose gardening,*
and when I think of my mother now she is often in the
garden, weeping, no, *weeding.* There was a special tool for
clipping the edges of the lawn. It had dark red handles
and hung upside down on two nails in the garage. Above,
over the joists, were cardboard boxes filled with blocks of
carbolic soap, a more meaty red. My uncle and aunt came
for supper and we stood in the garden under a clear blue
sky and my mother remarked how often this happens, a
grey day of drizzle and then quite suddenly at seven in
the evening the sun comes out.

39   These too: moments of grace or beauty that interrupt
the fabric of the day and suggest, well, just themselves
really, and the possibility that the world doesn't have to
be as grim as it makes out to be. They ambush me. They
are not supposed to be this ordinary. They make their
own demands. I take them home; I may need them later.
I add them to my collection of pebbles from the beach
that looked perfect when still wet. Sometimes I take them
down from the mantelpiece and dust them.

---

* Later, I did go with my mother to concerts of classical music. Not
many. I never worked out the silences – when I was supposed to
clap, when I was supposed to sit quiet and wait. I took my cue from
others.

40 'Hell for a poet is a soundproof room.' I remember that line from Louis MacNeice's *The Strings are False* but I may be wrong. I start looking for that book on my shelves and get distracted, as I often do, by Stendhal's *Memoirs of an Egotist*, a memoir that he started writing on 20 July 1832 and that proceeds from one distraction to another until, a fortnight later, mid-chapter, mid-paragraph, its subject the price of handkerchiefs, a full-on interruption: 'Half past one – it's become too hot to think.'

Distractions are horizontal. Interruptions are vertical: more oppositional, more push-back.

41 Stendhal wrote *The Charterhouse of Parma* in 53 days in late 1838 on the fourth floor (he favoured fourth floors) of number 8, rue de Caumartin, Paris, after instructing the concierge to tell any visitors that he'd gone hunting, because this was the only way to get the job done: he was a restless man with a low boredom threshold and a short attention span. Me too, but it's unlikely I'll buy one of those software programs that promise to block all distractions and allow me to concentrate on what might very loosely be called my 'project'. Without interruptions there *is* no project, except in the abstract.

42   Rain does love a good window. Clings to it. We sit and watch the rain, my father and I, and I try to explain how very, very hard it is to put onto a page even something as simple as the people walking by on the pavement. It's easy enough to seize on a detail – a sneeze, a stumble, a snazzy outfit – but each time I focus in close I'm interrupting the *flow*. My father thinks I'm talking about photography. He liked his cameras. He was interested in all the new gadgets. In the late 1940s he took many reels of movie film of war damage in Germany.

43   Sorry to interrupt, says Billie. She's in a novel I'm reading and she's not really sorry, she can't help herself. I'm reading along, minding my own business, and then Billie pipes up. We are all walking, talking interruptions of each other and of ourselves too. Each time I turn left I'm interrupting the lives I might have led if I'd turned right or carried straight on. Billie asks: Didn't I want, aged nine, to be a bus driver? If my father had lived longer, might I not have gone into the iron foundry business? And look what I've become – a writer? More a belletrist, I mumble, and she frowns. Still not a bus driver. And it wouldn't have been a bad life, driving the bus from village to village in the Yorkshire Dales, uphill and down, sunshine and rain . . .

44   Through the window of a train: I could live in that white house above the bay, in that flat with a bicycle on its balcony overlooking the track, in that new-build with not a scuff on its walls . . . Slippage may be my real subject here (books are often about something different from what they appear or claim to be about): between life and art, between things as they are and things as I'd prefer to believe they are, between blue sky and black rain. Here I go, continuously slip-sliding along streets paved with banana skins. Failure to distinguish – which is also success at not distinguishing (Coleridge's 'willing suspension of disbelief') – is cultivated by both art (the 'realist' modes are the most sly) and those in power, for whom fake news is usually preferable to any other kind.

45   I ask my father if he can remember a single book that he's read and he thinks for a while and then tells me about a book in which a child finds a stranger hiding in an outbuilding, a shed or a garage, and each night the child brings food to the stranger, and maybe something to drink. That could be one of several books, I tell my father. Can he be more specific? One night the child takes food to the outbuilding and the stranger has gone. Or: for three nights in a row the stranger waits and the child doesn't come.

46 More slippage. When I read a novel there are three of us (at least) involved: me, the character I happen to be reading about, and the author. Sometimes I'm inside the head of the character; sometimes I think I know more about this character than the author does; sometimes this character answers back. Sometimes – often – I'm attending not to what the author is saying but to how they are saying it. As if, really, there's a difference. Sometimes I sense that I'm being watched from a high window across the street – this is the author watching, but when I turn to look up at that window there is no one there.

47 I'm much older than my father ever was but of course now that we're sitting together I'm still a child. A trick of the light? Time, rather, acting like a traffic cop, telling us to keep in line and no overtaking.

48 *You switch on the ignition, you check the rear-view mirror, and you set off. You stick to the Highway Code, on the whole, and you try not to run over anyone. If you have a puncture you pull over and change the wheel. No need to fetishise interruptions.*

49 'Where do you see yourself in five years' time?' That used to be a regular question at job interviews. Middle management? Sailing a yacht in the Med? Dead? The first was the right answer: just the right level of ambition, the show kept on the road, the mortgage payments ticked. I looked at the beige carpet, the cheap desk with its grommet hole for cables, the coffee mugs in the sink, and I panicked.

50   Meanwhile, my father is explaining the Bessemer Process. (It's to do with the manufacture of steel. It's odd, he remarks, the things you remember when you no longer have any earthly use for them.) Meanwhile, a Rothko has sold at auction for a new record price. Meanwhile, children are being killed by Russian bombs in Ukraine. Meanwhile, senior management are getting blotto on their away-day. Meanwhile, *back at the ranch*, the writer at their desk is trying to join everything up without using the word 'meanwhile'. Any joining-up is in the mind of the writer as impressed on the page and it convinces or it doesn't depending on how they say it. Any joining-up plays second fiddle to what MacNeice termed, in a poem in which he tied some of the meanwhiles together, 'the drunkenness of things being various'. John Ashbery's poetry, a reviewer once persuasively suggested to me, is analogous to how the mind works, and how we live, attention flickering from this to that, continual interruption.

51   There aren't many social situations in which I don't feel I'm an interloper, interrupting a party that was proceeding quite happily until I turned up.

52   Most writers killed in traffic accidents, or who died from injuries sustained in these, have been men: Barthes, Camus, Jean Follain, Randall Jarrell, T. E. Lawrence, Frank O'Hara, Sebald, Svevo and Nathanael West for starters. Well, obviously: more male writers have been published than female. Or maybe women are just better drivers, and better at looking both ways before they cross the road. On the other hand, I can think of at least three novels by men in which both the wife and daughter of the main character (male) are randomly killed: in a car crash on an icy road, in a fire, in an explosion on a plane. The rapid interruption of women's lives is almost a genre.

53   'But' – the word is a frog. 'I think what you are trying to say is . . .' Women are interrupted by men more often than men by women. Frogs and toads migrating to their breeding grounds in spring can bring traffic to a halt. They stopped me and my bicycle one day in Golden Acre Park, and I may have squashed a few. Photographs of Golden Acre in the 1930s show fairground rides, dodgem cars, a boating lake, an outdoor swimming pool, a miniature railway: Coney Island, just north of Leeds.

By the 1960s it was a park where people in sensible shoes walked their dogs and occasionally let them off the lead.

54   In 27 April 1967 Susanna Kaysen had an appointment with a doctor she had never seen before and a lunch date. Lunch didn't happen. The doctor – 'a taut fat man, tight-bellied and dark' – claimed that he spoke with Kaysen for three hours. Years later, she discovered from her case notes that she was admitted to McLean psychiatric hospital for treatment for depression at 11.30 a.m. She remained there for two years. The session with the doctor lasted 20 minutes, half an hour at most. 'I won't quibble over ten minutes': *Girl, Interrupted* (1993).

55   Half-built villas are a vernacular feature in many rural districts in Europe, their completion interrupted by corruption or greed or poverty or stupidity. They look little different from villas half-destroyed in warfare. The stairs go nowhere: stubby concrete pillars, rusting steel rods, crushed beer cans and cigarette packets and dried turds in the corners. I dreamt that three of Danilo's sheep had trodden on landmines but no children so far, touch wood, and there was a game that became a craze among the girls from the village. While the boys raced bikes or mooched in bars, the girls skipped through the fences surrounding the villas and charmed the starving dogs, they ran onto the verandas and up the stairs and jumped off. They *leapt*. They fell on hard ground, stones, scrub, barbed wire grown over by bushes. Crippled for life, some of those girls.

56   A stone thrown through a window is a standard interruption in fiction.* In Paula Fox's *Desperate Characters* it arrives into a bedroom in which a psychoanalyst and a lawyer's wife have been quoting Baudelaire. In Gilbert Adair's *The Dreamers* it arrives into a bedroom in which three teenagers have been playing games based on films and having sex every which way. 'It sprayed the bed with fragments of glass.' Clunkily, the stones crashing through windows represent the intrusion of what's sometimes called 'real life'. Who threw them? The authors, of course.

57   Characters in novels who lean heavily upon art tend to get short shrift. The 'shards of broken glass' left by the stone through the window in *Desperate Characters* come less than a page after the quoting of Baudelaire.

---

* Different from that other stones-and-windows scene in which a lover throws pebbles at but not through an upstairs bedroom window, wanting to wake the belovèd but not the parents. How hard does the lover throw? The first throw is always too timid. Try again. I'm well aware that the woman – throwing stones tends to be a boy thing, being woken up a girl thing – may just want to get a good night's sleep.

The young cinéastes in *The Dreamers* bond through their shared love of watching films but 'the screen really was a screen. It screened them from the world.' Read my books, the authors are saying, but don't kid yourself.

58 Here is Laurence Sterne starting as he means to go on, making a point of not getting to the point, on the first page of *Tristram Shandy*: on a Sunday evening in March 1718 Tristram's mother and father are reaching the very moment of conceiving him when – '*Pray my Dear*, quoth my mother, *have you not forgot to wind up the clock? – Good G—!* cried my father, making an exclamation, but taking care to moderate his voice at the same time, – *Did ever woman, since the creation of the world, interrupt a man with such a silly question?*'

The question wasn't silly. The first Sunday of each month was when Mr S, 'one of the most regular men in all he did', wound the clock; and being 'somewhere between fifty and sixty years of age', he 'had brought some other family concernments to the same period, in order, as he would often say to my uncle Toby, to get them all out of the way at the same time'. For both Mr and Mrs Shandy, sex and clock-winding have become as apple and pear, rhubarb and custard, and although Mr S almost certainly *has* wound the clock Mrs S has mild hearing loss and may not be clocking the reassuring ticktock and has every right to ask.

59   Mr and Mrs Shandy's coitus interruptus – but not quite: though 'scattered and dispersed', enough 'animal spirits' still found their way to get little Tristram started – is there on page 1 to advertise that neither making babies nor living a life is a straightforward activity. Nor is writing about these activities. The trick to writing well about sex, I was once advised, is always to remember that other things are going on at the same time. Someone is playing a trombone. Someone in the street is feeling for his wallet and it's not there. Someone is eating crayfish.

60   I was on the top deck of a bus in Brighton when holes started to appear in the building I was looking at, the Royal Sussex County Hospital. The holes were smouldering, as if the building was a sheet of tissue paper on which ash from a lit cigarette had fallen, and some of them were joining up to make larger holes. This wasn't painful or even frightening, though I do remember thinking that if it got worse then at least the hospital was just over the road, if it hadn't burned down by the time I'd got off the bus. And then the lights changed or the traffic eased and the bus moved on and I have never experienced this again.

61   For most of human history, if war or disease didn't get you there was still fire or famine. It's only in the West, where governments claim that their chief priority is my 'safety and convenience' – my freedom to spend my money as I choose – that people have grown so used to dying peacefully in bed at a decent age that they take it for a human right. It is.

62   They'll win, won't they, the interruptions? Mostly it's low-level guerrilla warfare but the nuclear option is available and they're not handicapped by having to make risk assessments or distinctions between right and wrong. They have no point to prove, no act to get together.

63   A woman passing by the café table at which I'm reading asks me for a cigarette. Her name is Banana and mine, she tells me, is Ice Cream. I put down my book, I give her a cigarette. Half-turning away to hide what she's doing, but in a way that invites me to *see* what she is doing, she inserts the cigarette into an almost full pack of Marlboros. She is flirting with me. I go back to my book.

64   In the early years after I stopped writing poems* a

---

* A poem that didn't get written before the muse departed was titled 'Early Modern'. It was about the end of the feudal system and voyages of exploration and the beginning of scientific enquiry and adolescence, basically, while still holding on to comfort blankets. And still burning witches. I didn't know how to do it. Arrested development.

few lines slipped through, as if at the doorway the man I used to be had turned and begun to say something more before leaving but then thought better of it. Later, there were occasional lines by someone else entirely, who I never got to know. Then silence, no further interruptions.

65 Odysseus gets up, goes for a pee, brushes his teeth and sets off again from one real or imagined island in the Mediterranean to another, on this sea which is now a perfect storm of luxury cruise liners, cargo ships, inflatable life-rafts packed with refugees from slaughter and famine and slavery, police and coast-guard vessels, oligarchs' yachts, effluent, jellyfish, plastic waste, sometimes a fishing boat. Migrants from impoverished countries to countries implicated in that impoverishment, and profiting from it, are perceived as a threat to 'our way of life'. Power perpetuates power, controls the narrative and responds to criticism with 'Stop interrupting me' and normalises its own interruptions in any progress towards justice to the extent that we live in a permanent state of interruption.*

---

* This is Gramsci's interregnum, a perpetual one, between the old dying and the new which cannot be born, when 'a great variety of morbid symptoms' appear. My doctor shrugs. There's not much she can do for me. She could send me for some tests, she suggests, but we both know she's just going through the motions.

66 *Le Palais de Justice.* In August 1944 Samuel Beckett was a member of an Irish Red Cross team in the northern French town of Saint-Lô. He reported that 'Saint-Lô was bombed out of existence in one night'. Following the Allied invasion of Normandy, almost all of the town had been destroyed by American airpower; after its capture by American ground troops, what was left was pounded by German bombing raids. The text of Beckett's 'The Capital of the Ruins' was discovered in the archives of Radio Telefís Éireann in 1983 and according to the editor of *The Complete Short Prose* remains 'shrouded in mystery, confusion, and error'.

St-LO   Le Palais de Justice

67 Not all interruptions are sudden. Like illnesses, or 'economic modernisation', some are so gradual that for a while I'm not aware they are happening, and even when I do become suspicious I'm reluctant to do anything about them because I'm so wedded to a status quo in which I'm all right, Jack.

68 My father wants to go into the camera shop over the road but I'm feeling protective: he won't understand either the technology or the prices, and about the man who has run that shop for decades I have an uneasy feeling.* Something happened: blackmail (photos were involved), or embezzlement or even espionage, no one remembers exactly and it doesn't put off the Japanese tourists but there's a whiff of old-time scandal still lingering in the doorway like mist or a curtain, which is the opposite of a window.

69 *Did* I forget to wind the clock? All those things I should have done that I didn't do, and the ones I did that I shouldn't have done. I'm on the escalator at Angel tube, a long one, and I'm having a moment.

---

* I could take my father into the bookshop instead but I have an uneasy feeling about that place too. I get nervous in bookshops. All those *books* and some of them are laughing at me and it's catching. Bookshops are the watering-holes of my tribe so I *should* feel comfortable and there, perhaps, is the rub.

70 'The moment you realise that the train you are in is about to slow down and come to a stop in the middle of nowhere.' And no one is going to tell you why or for how long. That was one of around a dozen sentences that Gilbert Adair sent to his publisher as a proposal for a book (provisionally titled *The Middle of Nowhere*): each sentence was to be teased out in a few paragraphs of Adair's exquisite prose. Also in the list: 'The moment you realise absolutely no one is going to laugh at the joke you're telling'; 'The moment you trip over your own feet in the street'. Interruptions of forward momentum, all of them. The moment your publisher looks up from your book proposal and you can tell he just doesn't get it.

71 I'm in a holding space. A woman is hanging red and silver balls on a plastic Christmas tree. Another woman comes out of a door, glances at me, looks at the cover of the file she is carrying, goes back into the room she came out of. A man comes out of another door, turns to lock it, tells me his colleague will be with me soon, heads off to lunch. A third woman comes out of another door and locks it behind her; she is clutching tissues to her face, she has a nosebleed; she unlocks the door the man came out of and goes in. The Christmas-tree woman is now arranging strands of tinsel around framed advertisements for mortgages and pensions. I ask her how much longer I will need to sit here and she looks at me as if that is a question that no one in the history of the world has ever asked before. Together, we notice flecks of blood on the carpet. 'Festive,' she says.

72 Spoken language includes the interruptions: *ums* and *ers*, sneezes and hiccups, stumbles and stammers. Written language edits them out. Novelists, by indirect means, attempt to put them back in.

Many novelists have an aversion to finishing books. (Typically, Stendhal either skipped them, moving on to something ese, or rushed them, mashing everything together in a pile-up.) Some readers too.

Like children working out the world, which bit goes where, novelists often get it wrong but in interesting ways and you can't stop them trying.

Despite their constructed sense of inevitability, all novels contain the possibility that – if it hadn't been raining, if X hadn't knocked over a glass of wine or Y had been looking the other way – everything could have turned out differently.

73 The problem with finishing a book, for both writer and reader, is that it is finished: over, done, ticked off, stick it on a shelf or take it to a charity shop. For a book that we – writer, reader – have invested in, we have to be *ready* for it to end and we rarely are: wrong time of day and we're wearing the wrong clothes. The book has been saying, sentence by sentence, this is life; or at the very least, these are the lives of these people; and then it is not, it's just a piece of furniture. A chair, a wardrobe, a thing that gathers dust. I like very much that when people (critics included) relate to others the narrative of the books they have read, the films they have watched, they use the present tense: 'And then Eric goes to a bar and meets someone, and then Ada discovers her birth mother, and then Napoleon invades Russia' – as if everything within the book or film is still happening and there's no end in sight.

74 Tourists on a passing pleasure boat are waving and my brother and I, standing on the river bank, wave back because it would be rude not to. They'll soon be gone, past the bend in the river – but no, the boat is slowing down, and now it's beginning to turn around. This is a tricky manoeuvre; the river isn't much wider than the boat is long; but now the pleasure boat is heading back towards town. My brother explains that the boat turned round not because the tourists had paid for just a one-hour trip and their time was up but because the Earth is flat and if the boat had gone beyond the bend in the river it would have sailed off the edge: no more Happy Hours, no more buffet breakfasts. Drowning, not waving. I should get to know my brother better.

75   Waiting for a train at Shepherds Bush, I'm reading Will Eaves's *The Absent Therapist* – 'a jostle of voices,' the cover blurb tells me – next to a woman speaking on her phone: 'That's Isobel all over, she always exaggerates the bad stuff, when did you hear her exaggerate anything *good*?' The effect is stereophonic. No one ever *just reads a book* unless they're under the bedclothes after lights-out or they've climbed to the top of a very tall tree, which is where Uncle Teo is sitting in Fellini's *Amarcord* and he's not reading a book, he's shouting 'I want a woman!' A doctor and a very small nun coax him down. 'Some days he's normal,' says the doctor, 'some days he's just like the rest of us.'

76   When the train or the bus arrives we step back, letting folk off, and then forward, giving space to those with Zimmer frames or buggies to board first while still pressing close, wanting to get in while there might be some seats. And after the doorway bottleneck we separate, claiming a little distance, choosing wherever possible to sit not *next* to strangers. Who is this *we*? Zoom out, above the city, and you (who is this *you*?) see us all going someplace, wending our separate ways at our different speeds, sometimes changing our minds and turning back, currents and cross-currents – and what's strange is how rarely we bump into one another, knock one another off course . . . Given how many rights-of-way and fast-track privileges are monopolised by, well,

the privileged, what's also strange is how few people are
going berserk on the pavements with machetes. How
few, really, of what the police call *incidents*. Given how
many bad drivers there are, and sharp edges and toxic
additives, what's also strange is how many children
survive into adulthood. Zoom back in, this time to
the kitchen window of a bungalow in high summer
where a small boy is watching ants crawling along the
window sill, hell-bent on spilt sugar – and however many
interruptions he puts in their way (a twig, a pebble, a
bottle cap) they continue to do their thing, to the sugar
and back, around and along, in some kind of orderly
feeding frenzy.

77   Conversations between two people in which only
one person's voice is recorded are the narrative method
of A. B. Yehoshua's novel *Mr Mani* – so that what I read
are stories shaped by the prompts and interruptions
of unheard interlocutors. In the first part of the novel
a pregnant woman, talking to her mother on a phone,
recounts her own interruptions (three!) of the attempted
suicide of the father of her boyfriend. (The man gives up;
it's not supposed to be this difficult.) A friend told me a
similar story: while driving, the mother of a friend of this
friend had a puncture, and she stopped the car in a layby.
She had never changed a wheel before. Parked further
up the layby there was another car, and she knocked
on the window on the passenger side. Slowly, the door

opened. The inside of the car was dense with fumes; a whisky bottle lay on the floor; she was interrupting a man in the process of killing himself, having attached one end of a hose to the car's exhaust and fed the other end through the window on his side of the car. She explained her problem, the problem with the punctured tyre. She may even have apologised to the man for interrupting him, I don't know. The man got out of his car and helped her to jack up her own car and remove the wheel with the puncture and replace it with the spare. And then: what was it he'd been so intent on doing? Oh, forget it. Another time.

78 One afternoon in a bar on the umpteenth floor of a hotel in Manhattan Elizabeth Bowen glanced up from her bourbon and saw a suicide fall past the window. Of course she didn't know, in the moment of seeing, *what* she was seeing: a rapid shadow, an interruption of the light through the window.

79 Clackety-clack, clackety-clack, and then lightning strikes or the earth opens up or my credit card is blocked or I fall in love or it's Monday and the museum is closed and I have two hours to kill. At the café a one-legged pigeon comes pecking, a friend of the waiter who brings my coffee and who has only one arm. A man walks by with the exact profile of X, who I haven't thought of for years, maybe even decades, and I start wondering how many of the authors I admire were left-handed, or ticklish. I don't mean prickly in matters of etiquette, I mean wriggling and giggling when someone tickles you. Was Tolstoy ticklish? Eliot? The old bones in the museum, not to mention the pots and shards and the ornaments made from gold traded over half the world . . . I don't think there's a bone in my body that's dead straight.

80 Footnotes are interruptions – polite ones, knowing their place. The eye is pulled down to the bottom of the page, then released. I wrote a novel with footnotes, and sometimes footnotes to those footnotes. Then I wrote a book that comprised around a hundred pages of text, bristling with superscript numbers, followed by around 60 pages of small-print 'Notes and Asides'* – this was loosely modelled on a book by Walter de la Mare with more than 200 pages of notes riffing off phrases in a primary text of just 50 pages. A reader complained about the structure of my book: having to keep turning to a page at the back of the book meant that she had to keep interrupting herself. The *TLS* reviewer also didn't like it: 'Copious, inventive, incidental footnotes take up the final third of the book – maddeningly, since the reader

---

* Some of the best material was in the notes. Writer as smuggler: avoiding the official routes, sneaking the contraband in.

is forced to follow both the book and its wobbly shadow simultaneously.' It shouldn't be that difficult. Yehuda Amichai (in 'Nina of Ashkelon'): 'If we are trained well, we can do three or four things together at the same time: ride in a car, cry, and look through a window; eat, love, think.'

81   *The link you followed may be broken, or the page may have been removed.*

82   Where's Harry? He's not in today, says the woman from HR, he booked a day off. But I saw him in the canteen, says Ajay. The fire alarm has gone off and we are all standing in the car park at the fire assembly point, some of us smoking and some with takeaway coffees and can we go back to our desks soon, please? It's cold out here. A roll call is taken and there's no sign of Harry. Perhaps Harry is enjoying a lot of free food. Perhaps he's been burnt to a cinder. Perhaps this isn't just a rehearsal but the real thing. How will we know when it is?

83   There are gaps in the record. Every family tree has at least one blank space denoting someone who went out the back door, hopped on a train or a boat and was never seen or heard of again. When information is lacking the brain attempts to fill in the gaps by working from previous evidence, but often the big red vehicle I've seen approaching the stop turns out not to be a bus at all.

84   The gaps in the surviving texts of Sappho's poems are not just time's redactions, where sand-mites have nibbled the papyri, but are there because words fail, or stall. We know this instinctively and it is a big part of the poems' appeal. Words are fine for passing the time of day, less so for the time of night.

85   Memory as an instrument is both delicate and ruthless. From novels and films as well as life I remember only *the bits when*. The bit when the small boy comes into the narrator's room and looks around and then leaves. The bit when they're all in a garden in south London in April talking about love and trains. The bit when the man, sitting at a table opposite a boy who is refusing to eat a boiled egg, breaks down in tears. The bit with the dog. The pram bump-bumping down the Odessa Steps. The context for these bits, the overall narrative, has evaporated. The ligaments, the tendons, all the connective tissue has rotted away, leaving only a few pale bones.

86   I remember daddy-long-legs spiders in the front porch and hay fever and the taste of cod-liver oil. My father asks if I remember the time he carried me (aged four) on his shoulders into the iron foundry and I screamed in terror and yes, I do remember, not so much the burning fiery furnace, more that I spent the rest of the morning in the office, playing with a stapler while waiting to be taken home. I remember asking my granny – I was six years old and she was coming down the stairs, which had a rust-red carpet – whether it was it better to be a man or a woman. I don't remember her answer. I remember a moment in my twenties when it occurred to me that however long I lived it was possible that I would never be more happy than I was, right then. Over the door to the room, wrought-iron scrollwork.

87   'Why?' asks the child, and after the tired or impatient grown-up has answered 'Because I say so' the child keeps asking 'Why? Why?' – having sensed a weakness here, a loophole, having learned that often there is *no good answer* to why things are the way they are. And besides, the simple joy of interrupting and causing annoyance, which is more fun than listening to answers. When matters are let in place for so long that they come to be accepted as the 'natural' way of things it takes an awful lot of interruptions – enough to build up a momentum of their own, which itself invites interruption – to effect change. Start early, save lives.

88   I'd won the Nobel Prize in literature and everyone
was so embarrassed that we all agreed to pretend that it
hadn't happened. It was corrected to the Nobel Prize in
physics but that still didn't work. That was an unusual
dream; more common are those in which I nearly, so very
nearly, get the prize but don't. My frustration dreams
are often sexual and I worry about this because the last
thing sex is about is winning prizes. In a series of rooms
and corridors – and recently in a sort of holiday camp or
barracks – she and I, consenting adults, are forever *almost*
together and forever being interrupted by house guests
or football supporters or a man with a clipboard. Even
within these dreams I'm thinking, this is stupid, time to
wake up, please. Dreams are as hidebound by convention
as any genre.*

89   Fifty-one years is not a good age to die. Nor is it
any comfort to know that many books started by writers
never get finished, and most of the ones that do get
finished never get published. What happens to those
books, my father wants to know – are they just thrown
out on the street? Generally, yes.

---

* There was a period in childhood when I was able to dream
serially – I could go to bed and pick up a dream from where I'd left
off the previous night. Now, most of my dreams evaporate before I
can remember them; in the way that sometimes I *get it* – a sudden
and piercing understanding of how the world works – and then I
open my hand and it's empty.

90   I was standing in an empty flat in a tower block scheduled for demolition in East London because a writer had sent me some poems titled by number and asked if I'd like to see more – yes: please send #7, #22 and #114 – and the writer was also an artist and had invited me to a show of her work. On the walls were framed pages of hand-drawn grids; some of the squares were coloured in and each page was dated – they were records of a sort, temperature charts, or charts of sightings of polar bears in Alaska. Maybe the poems I'd asked for were among the blank squares, not yet written or coloured in, and maybe they never would be and that was the point: nothing there to record, or something there but the recording apparatus wasn't sophisticated enough to pick it up – unless they're up close, polar bears are hard to spot against snow – but the artist wasn't there to ask. A neighbour from the adjoining flat, one of the few people still living in the building, came in and asked what I thought of the work and we stood on the walkway to smoke and look out over London on a grey afternoon. Canary Wharf was still there, not moved very far from where it was last time I looked.

91   Literary forms as *resistance* to life's formlessnesss?* No heavy artillery: this is guerrilla resistance against a

---

* My father tells me I have a thing about how books relate to life. I really don't. I protest too much, he says, and he has a point. Raised

force that is infinitely larger so books may as well just go for it, using camouflage and booby traps and every trick up their sleeve. But literary forms are stamped with human fingerprints and resistant to the anti-life notion of glossy perfection, so books and life are on the same side after all? Ken Garland had a photo in his flat of people sitting around a table in the middle of a field talking, eating, drinking, arguing, joking – freedom coexisting with social form, and *bon appétit*. I'll take that. How did the table and its white tablecloth get there? By accident, against incalculable odds.

92 'Did you sleep well?' I would have done, if it hadn't been for the foxes mating in the back yard, a pain in my gut and a nagging suspicion at 3 a.m. that I have wasted my life.

93 This is a big one: self-doubt. Not 'rudely interrupted' but *crippled* by self-doubt, *paralysed* by self-doubt. The engine starts spluttering and I pull over onto the hard shoulder, where it judders to a halt. The car is

---

in a Protestant family and living in a narrowly capitalist society that expects me to justify myself on the grounds that I'm contributing to the national economy (hardly) or, going the other way, that the books I make give life meaning or add some extra-curricular value (sometimes, but don't count on it), of course I protest.

kaput: it may never get moving again. I sit on the litter-strewn verge watching the traffic speed by. It's raining.

94   If the weather is fine, after Sunday lunch we might go for a 'drive'. Trees and cows and electricity pylons. Sometimes we get stuck behind a tractor but we are not in a hurry, we're not *going* anywhere. The car has a glove compartment and the roundabouts have flower beds. When we come to a junction I don't know how my mother knows which way to turn, she just does. Granny has gone to sleep and when she wakes up she'll say she feels 'refreshed'.

95   Driving down to Cornwall, there is a point on the A303 where I come over the brow of a hill and spread out before me is my mother's England – wide, endless, but also domesticated, tidy, *kempt*: the fields patchwork-quilted, the villages within their parish bounds, the little roads tucked in. And the traffic is swishing, swishing past me, the big lorries rocking the car.

96   My father is getting restless. He asks if I think we're sitting here together just by chance? Shouldn't we be heading towards some kind of, how to put this, resolution? Is there something he should be telling me? Is there something I should be telling him, and I've

forgotten? What are my books *about*? How long does it take to write one? How many copies do I sell? How can I tell if my books are any good? Do I sometimes think – and he doesn't mean this personally,* he's just curious – that I'm kidding myself? If yes, does that matter? Who decides? Does this place serve alcohol? What time is the last bus?

97   Little interruptions at the last minute. In Penelope Fitzgerald's short story 'The Means of Escape' a convict in Tasmania makes good his escape with a woman encountered by chance just before he boards a ship bound for England; in Edgardo Cozarinsky's 'The Bride from Odessa' a man from Ukraine leaves for Argentina with another woman encountered by chance at the port. Both men have promised different women that they will send for them once they are established in their new countries and neither does this. Love, lack of love, destiny, whatever. Both stories are set in the late 19th century and so open up the long perspective: I am here and I am me because one rainy evening one of my great-great-grandparents asked a stranger for a light at a bus stop.

---

* But it is personal. At least, it is to me. My father made cast-iron drainpipes, I make books, so as well as the fact that he is officially dead and I am not there is what might be called a socio-economic difference here. I don't want to get into that just now – another time. My father shrugs.

98   I found the photograph of students in a classroom (see **36**) in a junk shop in the Czech Republic and I'm guessing it was taken in the 1930s. A Tuesday morning. Cloudy, occasional showers. There will be a war and these young men will be called on to fight and some will be killed and the professor's retirement party will be bleak, with cheap wine in plastic cups. But right now I could walk into that room and they wouldn't even look up.

99   The rain has stopped. It was only a shower. My father is not a *senior* rain god. He looks at his watch – a modern one, not the 1930s Longines I inherited and which may not even have been his and which needs winding up every day – and leaves.

Founded in 2007, CB editions publishes chiefly short
fiction and poetry, including work in translation.
Books can be ordered from www.cbeditions.com.